BIG SCREEN THEMES

MUSIC FROM THE MOVIES FOR S

CW00348626

WISE PUBLICATIONS
PART OF THE MUSIC SALES GROUP

LONDON / NEW YORK / PARIS / SYDNEY / COPENHAGEN / BERLIN / MADRID / TOKYO

Published by

Wise Publications
14-15 Berners Street, London W1T 3LJ, UK

Exclusive Distributors:

Music Sales Limited
Distribution Centre, Newmarket Road,
Bury St Edmunds, Suffolk IP33 3YB, UK

Music Sales Pty Limited
20 Resolution Drive,
Caringbah, NSW 2229, Australia

Order No. AM998602
ISBN 978-1-84938-252-6
This book © Copyright 2009 Wise Publications,
a division of Music Sales Limited.

Edited by Jenni Wheeler.
Cover designed by Liz Barrand.

Printed in the EU

www.musicsales.com

Your Guarantee of Quality
As publishers, we strive to produce every book
to the highest commercial standards.
The music has been freshly engraved and the book has
been carefully designed to minimise awkward page turns
and to make playing from it a real pleasure.
Particular care has been given to specifying acid-free,
neutral-sized paper made from pulps which have not been
elemental chlorine bleached. This pulp is from farmed
sustainable forests and was produced with special regard
for the environment.
Throughout, the printing and binding have been planned
to ensure a sturdy, attractive publication which should
give years of enjoyment.
If your copy fails to meet our high standards,
please inform us and we will gladly replace it.

ANDANTE/REFLECTION (END TITLE)
(FROM 'WALTZ WITH BASHIR')
MUSIC BY MAX RICHTER

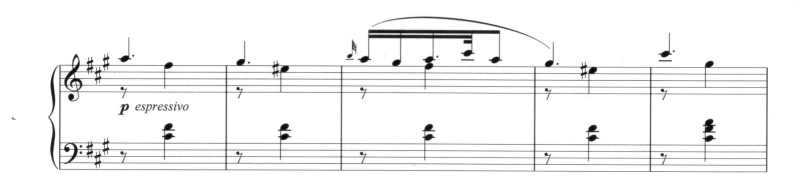

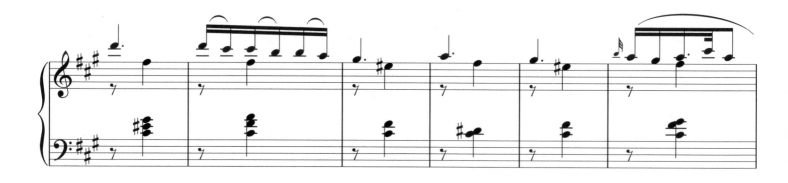

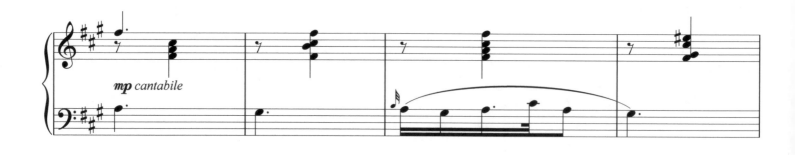

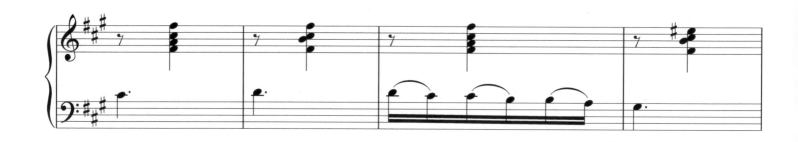

Benjamin And Daisy
(FROM 'THE CURIOUS CASE OF BENJAMIN BUTTON')
MUSIC BY ALEXANDRE DESPLAT

D.S. al Coda   **Coda**

9

Dawn/Going To School

(FROM 'GENOVA')

MUSIC BY MELISSA PARMENTER

13

GOING TO SCHOOL

DEATH AND TRANSFIGURATION
(FROM 'HANCOCK')
MUSIC BY JOHN POWELL

18

The Egg/Cycling Holiday
(FROM 'THE READER')
MUSIC BY NICO MUHLY

THE EGG
Moderato ♩ = 100

DMI Thing In Which New Information Is Introduced/Piano One

(from 'Synecdoche, New York')

MUSIC BY JON BRION

Eli's Theme
(FROM 'LET THE RIGHT ONE IN')
MUSIC BY JOHAN SÖDERQVIST

The International (End Title)
(from 'The International')

Music by Matthew Bellamy, Tom Tykwer,
Johnny Klimek & Reinhold Heil

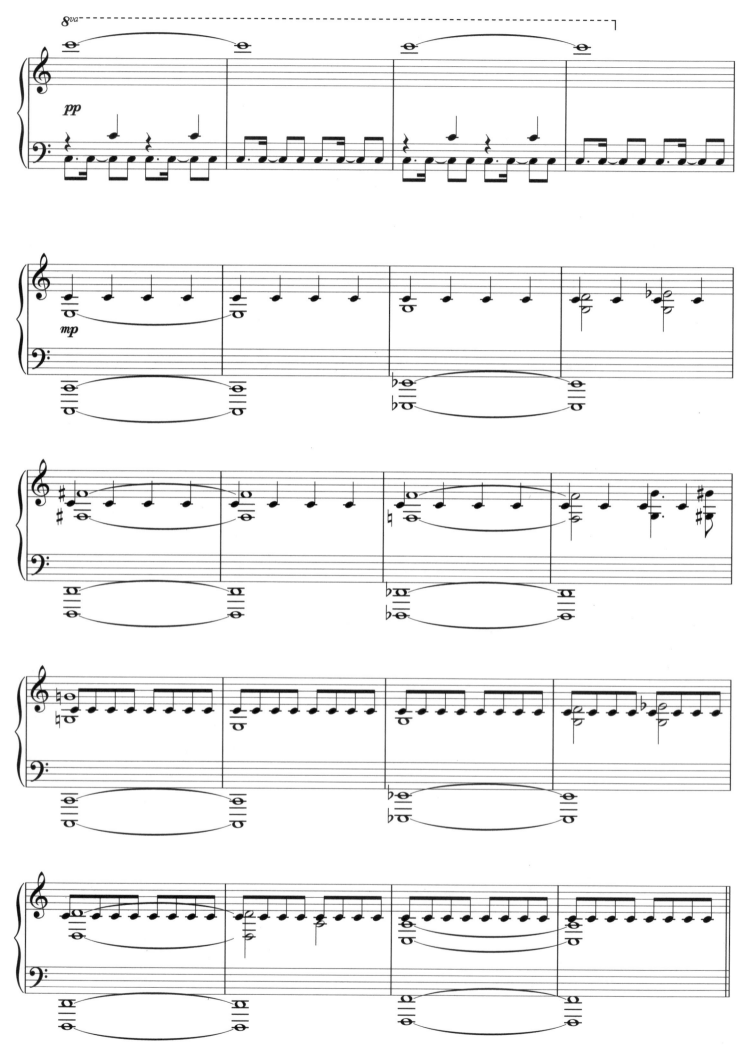

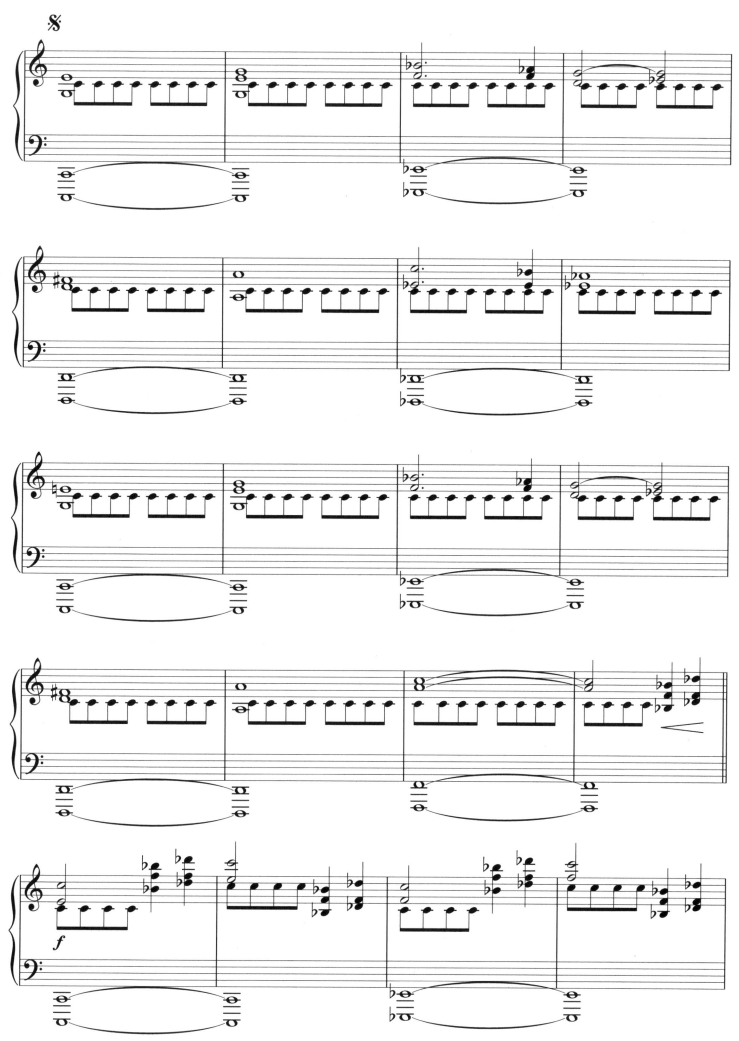

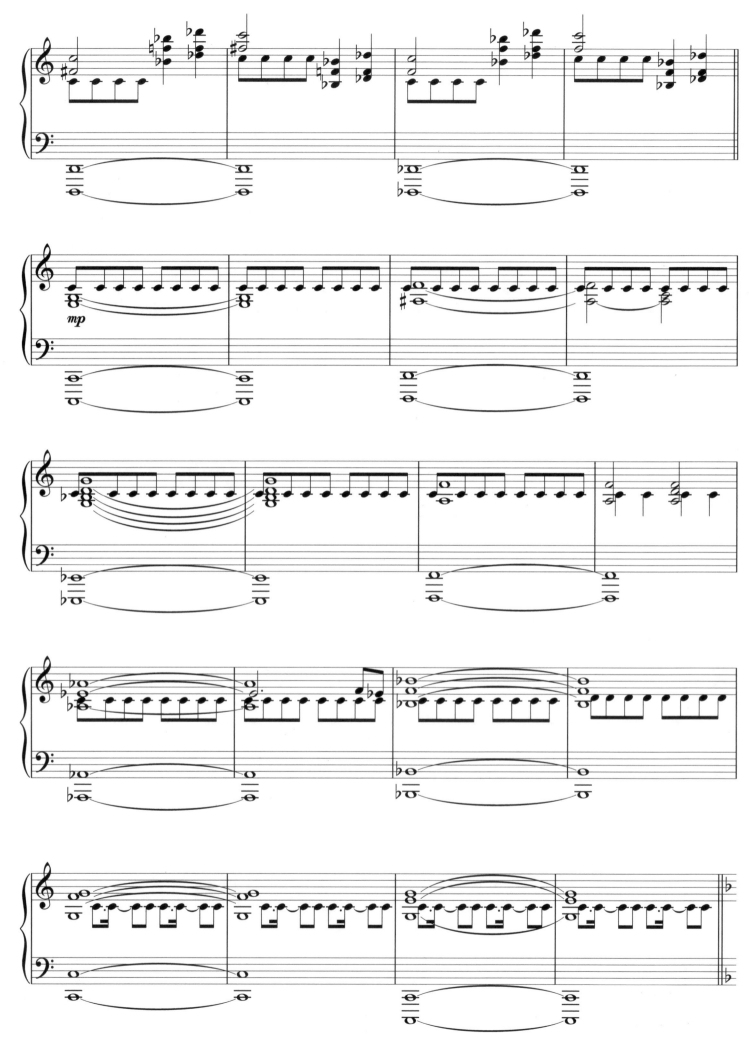

33

To Coda ⊕

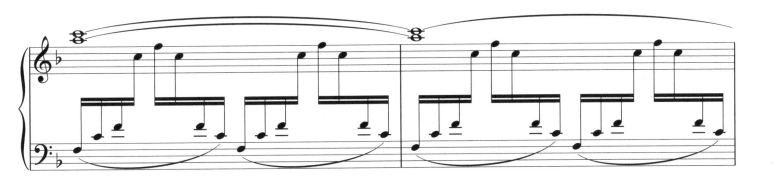

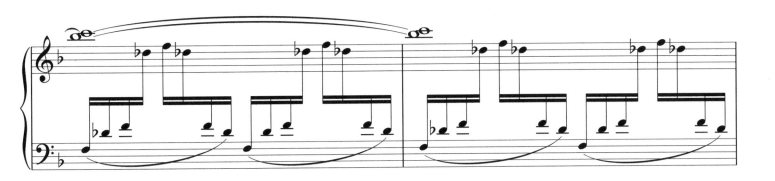

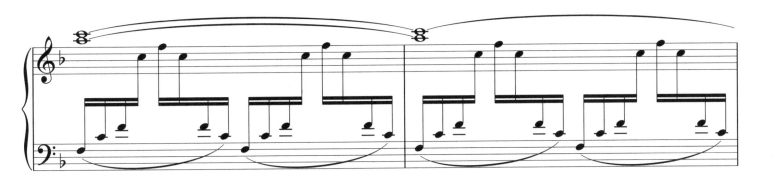

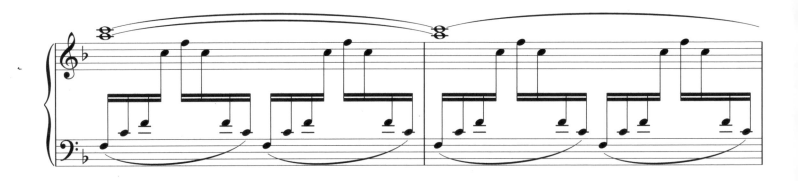

D.S. al Coda

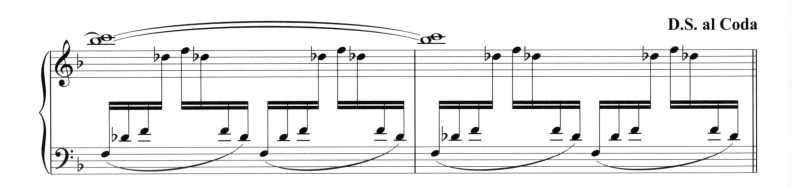

⊕ Coda

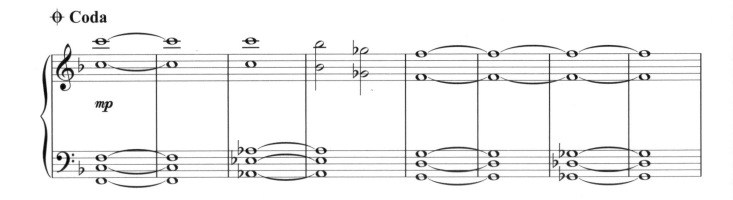

Fly A Kite/Reading The Letter

(FROM 'THE KITE RUNNER')

MUSIC BY ALBERTO IGLESIAS

40

41

Harvey's Last Day
(FROM 'MILK')

MUSIC BY DANNY ELFMAN

In The Library
(FROM 'EASY VIRTUE')
MUSIC BY MARIUS DE VRIES

Swing feel ♩. = 90

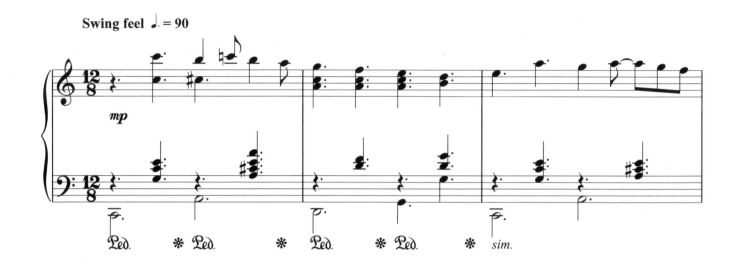

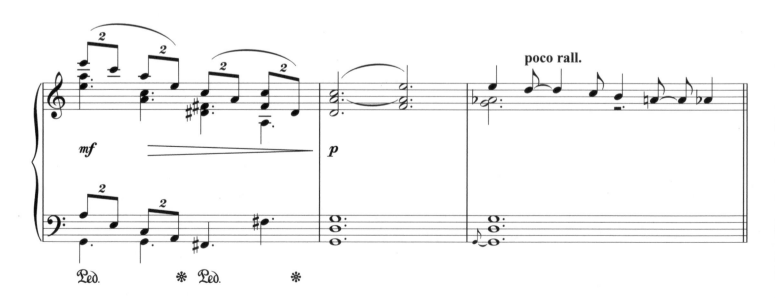

49

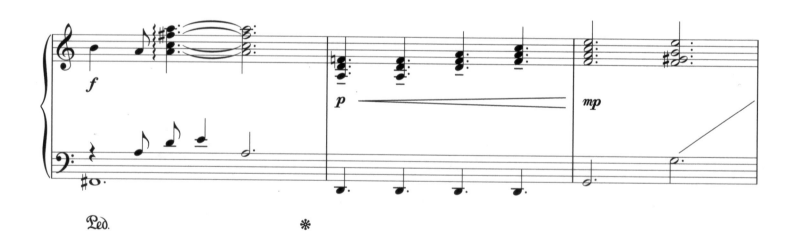

PROLOGUE/WALKING IN BRUGES/
RAY AT THE MIRROR

(FROM 'IN BRUGES')

MUSIC BY CARTER BURWELL

53

Latika's Theme
(from 'Slumdog Millionaire')

Music by A. R. Rahman

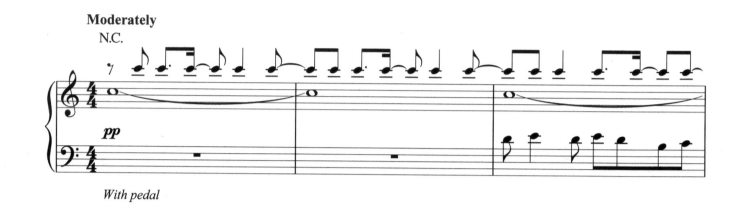

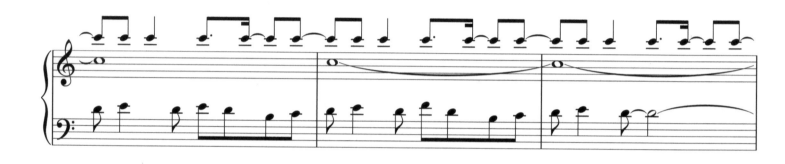

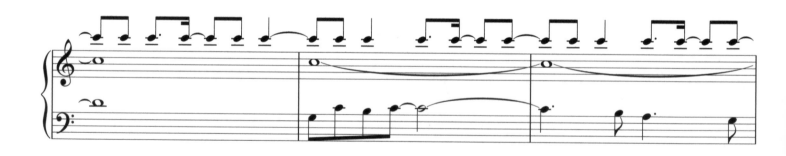

Minimal 4/Minimal 8
(from 'Blindness')
Music by Marco Antônio Guimarães

MINIMAL 4

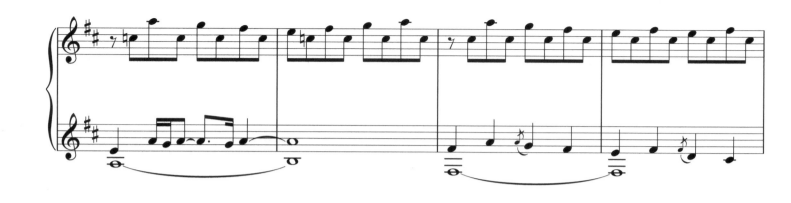

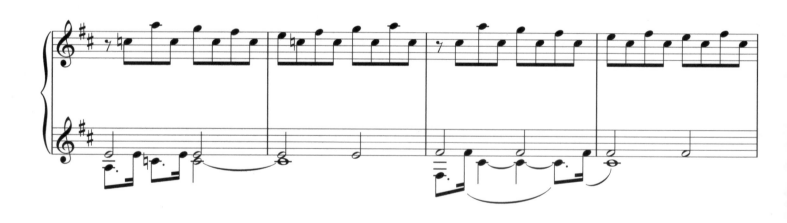

MINIMAL 8

Play 6 times

Sebastian
(FROM 'BRIDESHEAD REVISITED')
MUSIC BY ADRIAN JOHNSTON

65

Salvation

(FROM 'TERMINATOR SALVATION')

MUSIC BY DANNY ELFMAN

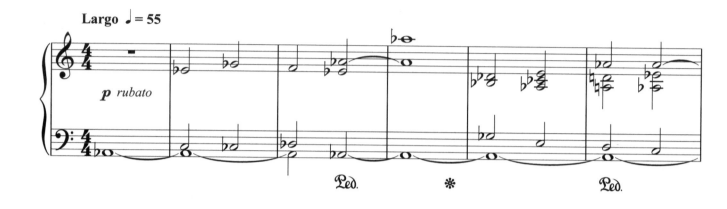

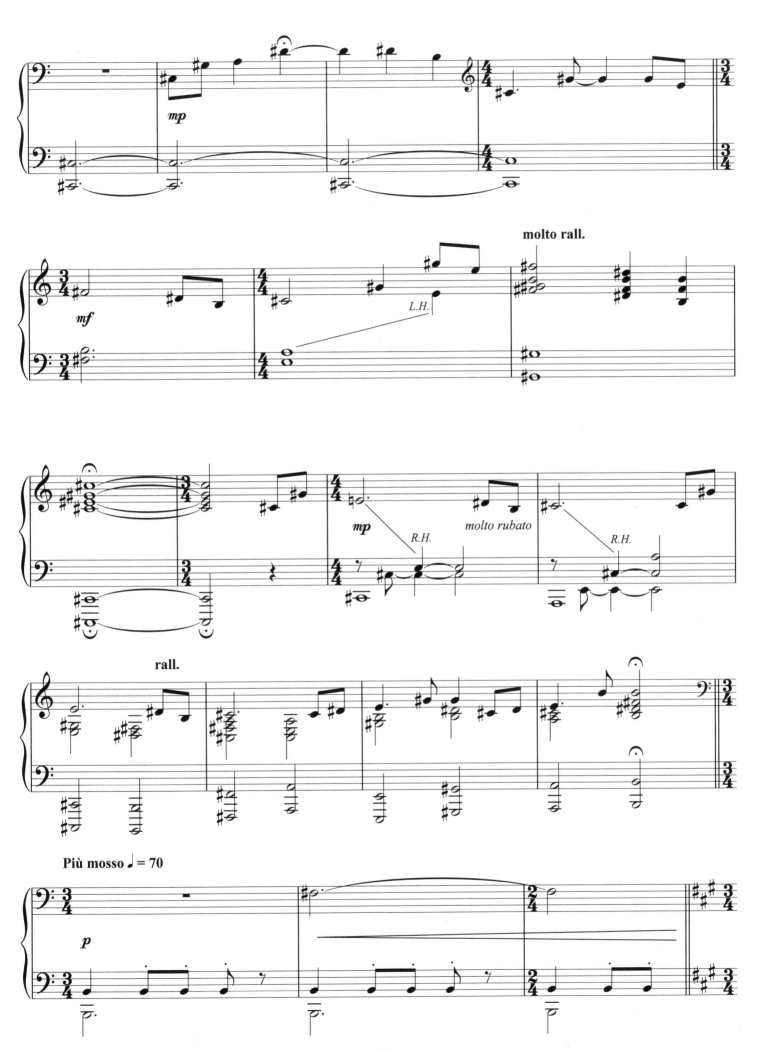

TELSTAR
(FROM 'TELSTAR')
MUSIC BY JOE MEEK

THAT NEW CAR SMELL

(FROM 'STAR TREK')

MUSIC BY MICHAEL GIACCHINO

THEN WE ARE TOGETHER
(FROM 'LET THE RIGHT ONE IN')
MUSIC BY JOHAN SÖDERQVIST

81

Walter's Etude No. 1
(FROM 'THE VISITOR')
MUSIC BY JAN A. P. KACZMAREK

Victoria And Albert
(FROM 'THE YOUNG VICTORIA')
MUSIC BY ILAN ESHKERI

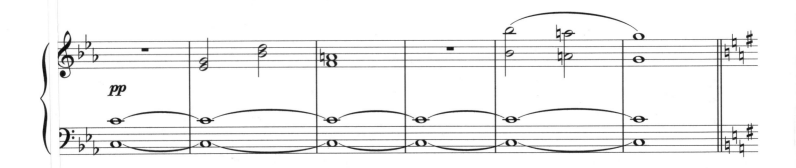

Ped.   ✶   Ped.   ✶

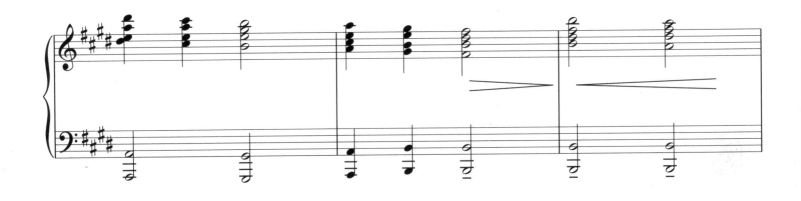

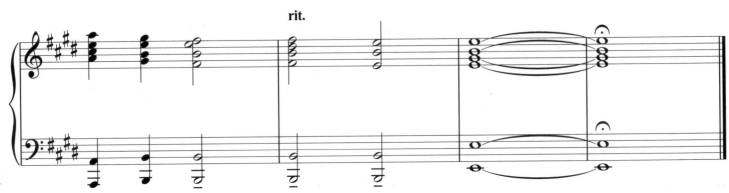

123456789